# PERSONAL INFORMATION

**NAME:**

**ADDRESS:**

**PHONE:**

**E-MAIL:**

# IN AN EMERGENCY PLEASE CONTACT

**NAME:**

**ADDRESS:**

**PHONE:**

**DOCTOR PHONE:**

**KNOWN ALLERGIES:**

# 2024

## JANUARY

| M | T | W | T | F | **S** | **S** |
|---|---|---|---|---|---|---|
| 1 | 2 | 3 | 4 | 5 | **6** | **7** |
| 8 | 9 | 10 | 11 | 12 | **13** | **14** |
| 15 | 16 | 17 | 18 | 19 | **20** | **21** |
| 22 | 23 | 24 | 25 | 26 | **27** | **28** |
| 29 | 30 | 31 | | | | |

## FEBRUARY

| M | T | W | T | F | **S** | **S** |
|---|---|---|---|---|---|---|
| | | | 1 | 2 | **3** | **4** |
| 5 | 6 | 7 | 8 | 9 | **10** | **11** |
| 12 | 13 | 14 | 15 | 16 | **17** | **18** |
| 19 | 20 | 21 | 22 | 23 | **24** | **25** |
| 26 | 27 | 28 | 29 | | | |

## MARCH

| M | T | W | T | F | **S** | **S** |
|---|---|---|---|---|---|---|
| | | | | 1 | **2** | **3** |
| 4 | 5 | 6 | 7 | 8 | **9** | **10** |
| 11 | 12 | 13 | 14 | 15 | **16** | **17** |
| 18 | 19 | 20 | 21 | 22 | **23** | **24** |
| 25 | 26 | 27 | 28 | 29 | **30** | **31** |

## APRIL

| M | T | W | T | F | **S** | **S** |
|---|---|---|---|---|---|---|
| 1 | 2 | 3 | 4 | 5 | **6** | **7** |
| 8 | 9 | 10 | 11 | 12 | **13** | **14** |
| 15 | 16 | 17 | 18 | 19 | **20** | **21** |
| 22 | 23 | 24 | 25 | 26 | **27** | **28** |
| 29 | 30 | | | | | |

## MAY

| M | T | W | T | F | **S** | **S** |
|---|---|---|---|---|---|---|
| | | 1 | 2 | 3 | **4** | **5** |
| 6 | 7 | 8 | 9 | 10 | **11** | **12** |
| 13 | 14 | 15 | 16 | 17 | **18** | **19** |
| 20 | 21 | 22 | 23 | 24 | **25** | **26** |
| 27 | 28 | 29 | 30 | 31 | | |

## JUNE

| M | T | W | T | F | **S** | **S** |
|---|---|---|---|---|---|---|
| | | | | | **1** | **2** |
| 3 | 4 | 5 | 6 | 7 | **8** | **9** |
| 10 | 11 | 12 | 13 | 14 | **15** | **16** |
| 17 | 18 | 19 | 20 | 21 | **22** | **23** |
| 24 | 25 | 26 | 27 | 28 | **29** | **30** |

## JULY

| M | T | W | T | F | **S** | **S** |
|---|---|---|---|---|---|---|
| 1 | 2 | 3 | 4 | 5 | **6** | **7** |
| 8 | 9 | 10 | 11 | 12 | **13** | **14** |
| 15 | 16 | 17 | 18 | 19 | **20** | **21** |
| 22 | 23 | 24 | 25 | 26 | **27** | **28** |
| 29 | 30 | 31 | | | | |

## AUGUST

| M | T | W | T | F | **S** | **S** |
|---|---|---|---|---|---|---|
| | | | 1 | 2 | **3** | **4** |
| 5 | 6 | 7 | 8 | 9 | **10** | **11** |
| 12 | 13 | 14 | 15 | 16 | **17** | **18** |
| 19 | 20 | 21 | 22 | 23 | **24** | **25** |
| 26 | 27 | 28 | 29 | 30 | **31** | |

## SEPTEMBER

| M | T | W | T | F | **S** | **S** |
|---|---|---|---|---|---|---|
| | | | | | | **1** |
| 2 | 3 | 4 | 5 | 6 | **7** | **8** |
| 9 | 10 | 11 | 12 | 13 | **14** | **15** |
| 16 | 17 | 18 | 19 | 20 | **21** | **22** |
| 23 | 24 | 25 | 26 | 27 | **28** | **29** |
| 30 | | | | | | |

## OCTOBER

| M | T | W | T | F | **S** | **S** |
|---|---|---|---|---|---|---|
| | 1 | 2 | 3 | 4 | **5** | **6** |
| 7 | 8 | 9 | 10 | 11 | **12** | **13** |
| 14 | 15 | 16 | 17 | 18 | **19** | **20** |
| 21 | 22 | 23 | 24 | 25 | **26** | **27** |
| 28 | 29 | 30 | 31 | | | |

## NOVEMBER

| M | T | W | T | F | **S** | **S** |
|---|---|---|---|---|---|---|
| | | | | 1 | **2** | **3** |
| 4 | 5 | 6 | 7 | 8 | **9** | **10** |
| 11 | 12 | 13 | 14 | 15 | **16** | **17** |
| 18 | 19 | 20 | 21 | 22 | **23** | **24** |
| 25 | 26 | 27 | 28 | 29 | **30** | |

## DECEMBER

| M | T | W | T | F | **S** | **S** |
|---|---|---|---|---|---|---|
| | | | | | | **1** |
| 2 | 3 | 4 | 5 | 6 | **7** | **8** |
| 9 | 10 | 11 | 12 | 13 | **14** | **15** |
| 16 | 17 | 18 | 19 | 20 | **21** | **22** |
| 23 | 24 | 25 | 26 | 27 | **28** | **29** |
| 30 | 31 | | | | | |

# NOTABLE DATES

## JANUARY

1  NEW YEAR'S DAY

2  NEW YEAR HOLIDAY
   (SCOTLAND)

## FEBRUARY

10  CHINESE NEW YEAR (DRAGON)

13  SHROVE TUESDAY

14  VALENTINE'S DAY

## MARCH

1  ST. DAVID'S DAY

8  INTERNATIONAL WOMEN'S DAY

10  MOTHER'S DAY (UK) &
    RAMADAN BEGINS

17  ST. PATRICK'S DAY

29  GOOD FRIDAY

31  EASTER SUNDAY &
    DAYLIGHT SAVING TIME STARTS

## APRIL

1  EASTER MONDAY

22  PASSOVER BEGINS

23  ST. GEORGE'S DAY

## MAY

6  EARLY MAY BANK HOLIDAY

27  SPRING BANK HOLIDAY

## JUNE

16  FATHER'S DAY (UK)

## JULY

6  ISLAMIC NEW YEAR BEGINS

12  PUBLIC HOLIDAY (NORTHERN
    IRELAND)

## AUGUST

5  SUMMER BANK HOLIDAY
   (SCOTLAND)

26  SUMMER BANK HOLIDAY
    (ENG, NIR, WAL)

## SEPTEMBER

21  INTERNATIONAL DAY OF PEACE
    (UNITED NATIONS)

## OCTOBER

2  ROSH HASHANAH (JEWISH NEW
   YEAR) BEGINS

10  WORLD MENTAL HEALTH DAY

11  YOM KIPPUR BEGINS

27  DAYLIGHT SAVING TIME ENDS

31  HALLOWEEN

## NOVEMBER

1  DIWALI

5  GUY FAWKES NIGHT

10  REMEMBRANCE SUNDAY

30  ST. ANDREW'S DAY

## DECEMBER

25  CHRISTMAS DAY

26  BOXING DAY

31  NEW YEAR'S EVE

# JANUARY

1 M
2 T
3 W
4 T
5 F
6 S
7 S
8 M
9 T
10 W
11 T
12 F
13 S
14 S
15 M
16 T
17 W
18 T
19 F
20 S
21 S
22 M
23 T
24 W
25 T
26 F
27 S
28 S
29 M
30 T
31 W

# FEBRUARY

1 T
2 F
3 S
4 S
5 M
6 T
7 W
8 T
9 F
10 S
11 S
12 M
13 T
14 W
15 T
16 F
17 S
18 S
19 M
20 T
21 W
22 T
23 F
24 S
25 S
26 M
27 T
28 W
29 T

# PLANNER

## MARCH

1 F
2 S
3 S
4 M
5 T
6 W
7 T
8 F
9 S
10 S
11 M
12 T
13 W
14 T
15 F
16 S
17 S
18 M
19 T
20 W
21 T
22 F
23 S
24 S
25 M
26 T
27 W
28 T
29 F
30 S
31 S

## APRIL

1 M
2 T
3 W
4 T
5 F
6 S
7 S
8 M
9 T
10 W
11 T
12 F
13 S
14 S
15 M
16 T
17 W
18 T
19 F
20 S
21 S
22 M
23 T
24 W
25 T
26 F
27 S
28 S
29 M
30 T

| | MAY | | | JUNE |
|---|---|---|---|---|
| 1 | W | | 1 | S |
| 2 | T | | 2 | S |
| 3 | F | | 3 | M |
| 4 | S | | 4 | T |
| 5 | S | | 5 | W |
| 6 | M | | 6 | T |
| 7 | T | | 7 | F |
| 8 | W | | 8 | S |
| 9 | T | | 9 | S |
| 10 | F | | 10 | M |
| 11 | S | | 11 | T |
| 12 | S | | 12 | W |
| 13 | M | | 13 | T |
| 14 | T | | 14 | F |
| 15 | W | | 15 | S |
| 16 | T | | 16 | S |
| 17 | F | | 17 | M |
| 18 | S | | 18 | T |
| 19 | S | | 19 | W |
| 20 | M | | 20 | T |
| 21 | T | | 21 | F |
| 22 | W | | 22 | S |
| 23 | T | | 23 | S |
| 24 | F | | 24 | M |
| 25 | S | | 25 | T |
| 26 | S | | 26 | W |
| 27 | M | | 27 | T |
| 28 | T | | 28 | F |
| 29 | W | | 29 | S |
| 30 | T | | 30 | S |
| 31 | F | | | |

# PLANNER

| JULY | AUGUST |
|------|--------|
| 1 M | 1 T |
| 2 T | 2 F |
| 3 W | 3 S |
| 4 T | 4 S |
| 5 F | 5 M |
| 6 S | 6 T |
| 7 S | 7 W |
| 8 M | 8 T |
| 9 T | 9 F |
| 10 W | 10 S |
| 11 T | 11 S |
| 12 F | 12 M |
| 13 S | 13 T |
| 14 S | 14 W |
| 15 M | 15 T |
| 16 T | 16 F |
| 17 W | 17 S |
| 18 T | 18 S |
| 19 F | 19 M |
| 20 S | 20 T |
| 21 S | 21 W |
| 22 M | 22 T |
| 23 T | 23 F |
| 24 W | 24 S |
| 25 T | 25 S |
| 26 F | 26 M |
| 27 S | 27 T |
| 28 S | 28 W |
| 29 M | 29 T |
| 30 T | 30 F |
| 31 W | 31 S |

**2024**

| SEPTEMBER | OCTOBER |
|---|---|
| 1 S | 1 T |
| 2 M | 2 W |
| 3 T | 3 T |
| 4 W | 4 F |
| 5 T | 5 S |
| 6 F | 6 S |
| 7 S | 7 M |
| 8 S | 8 T |
| 9 M | 9 W |
| 10 T | 10 T |
| 11 W | 11 F |
| 12 T | 12 S |
| 13 F | 13 S |
| 14 S | 14 M |
| 15 S | 15 T |
| 16 M | 16 W |
| 17 T | 17 T |
| 18 W | 18 F |
| 19 T | 19 S |
| 20 F | 20 S |
| 21 S | 21 M |
| 22 S | 22 T |
| 23 M | 23 W |
| 24 T | 24 T |
| 25 W | 25 F |
| 26 T | 26 S |
| 27 F | 27 S |
| 28 S | 28 M |
| 29 S | 29 T |
| 30 M | 30 W |
|  | 31 T |

# PLANNER

# NOVEMBER

1 F
2 S
3 S
4 M
5 T
6 W
7 T
8 F
9 S
10 S
11 M
12 T
13 W
14 T
15 F
16 S
17 S
18 M
19 T
20 W
21 T
22 F
23 S
24 S
25 M
26 T
27 W
28 T
29 F
30 S

# DECEMBER

1 S
2 M
3 T
4 W
5 T
6 F
7 S
8 S
9 M
10 T
11 W
12 T
13 F
14 S
15 S
16 M
17 T
18 W
19 T
20 F
21 S
22 S
23 M
24 T
25 W
26 T
27 F
28 S
29 S
30 M
31 T

2024

# JANUARY

**MON**
**1**

NEW YEAR'S DAY

**TUE**
**2**

NEW YEAR HOLIDAY (SCOTLAND)

**WED**
**3**

**THU**
**4**

**FRI**
**5**

**SAT**
**6**

**SUN**
**7**

# JANUARY

**MON**
**8**

---

**TUE**
**9**

---

**WED**
**10**

---

**THU**
**11**

---

**FRI**
**12**

---

**SAT**
**13**

---

**SUN**
**14**

# JANUARY

**MON**
**15**

**TUE**
**16**

**WED**
**17**

**THU**
**18**

**FRI**
**19**

**SAT**
**20**

**SUN**
**21**

# JANUARY

**MON**
**22**

---

**TUE**
**23**

---

**WED**
**24**

---

**THU**
**25**

---

**FRI**
**26**

---

**SAT**
**27**

---

**SUN**
**28**

# JAN / FEB

**MON**
**29**

**TUE**
**30**

**WED**
**31**

**THU**
**1**

**FRI**
**2**

**SAT**
**3**

**SUN**
**4**

# FEBRUARY

**MON**
**5**

**TUE**
**6**

**WED**
**7**

**THU**
**8**

**FRI**
**9**

**SAT**
**10**

CHINESE NEW YEAR (DRAGON)

**SUN**
**11**

# FEBRUARY

**MON**
**12**

---

**TUE**
**13**

SHROVE TUESDAY

---

**WED**
**14**

VALENTINE'S DAY

---

**THU**
**15**

---

**FRI**
**16**

---

**SAT**
**17**

---

**SUN**
**18**

# FEBRUARY

**MON**
**19**

**TUE**
**20**

**WED**
**21**

**THU**
**22**

**FRI**
**23**

**SAT**
**24**

**SUN**
**25**

# FEB / MAR

**MON**
**26**

**TUE**
**27**

**WED**
**28**

**THU**
**29**

**FRI**
**1**

ST. DAVID'S DAY

**SAT**
**2**

**SUN**
**3**

# MARCH

**MON**
**4**

**TUE**
**5**

**WED**
**6**

**THU**
**7**

**FRI**
**8**

INTERNATIONAL WOMEN'S DAY

**SAT**
**9**

**SUN**
**10**

MOTHER'S DAY (UK) & RAMADAN BEGINS

# MARCH

**MON**
**11**

**TUE**
**12**

**WED**
**13**

**THU**
**14**

**FRI**
**15**

**SAT**
**16**

**SUN**
**17**

ST. PATRICK'S DAY

# MARCH

**MON**
**18**

**TUE**
**19**

**WED**
**20**

**THU**
**21**

**FRI**
**22**

**SAT**
**23**

**SUN**
**24**

# MARCH

**MON 25**

**TUE 26**

**WED 27**

**THU 28**

**FRI 29**

GOOD FRIDAY

**SAT 30**

**SUN 31**

EASTER SUNDAY & DAYLIGHT SAVING TIME STARTS

# APRIL

**MON**
**1**

EASTER MONDAY

**TUE**
**2**

**WED**
**3**

**THU**
**4**

**FRI**
**5**

**SAT**
**6**

**SUN**
**7**

# APRIL

**MON**
8

**TUE**
9

**WED**
10

**THU**
11

**FRI**
12

**SAT**
13

**SUN**
14

# APRIL

**MON**
**15**

**TUE**
**16**

**WED**
**17**

**THU**
**18**

**FRI**
**19**

**SAT**
**20**

**SUN**
**21**

# APRIL

## MON
## 22

PASSOVER BEGINS

## TUE
## 23

ST. GEORGE'S DAY

## WED
## 24

## THU
## 25

## FRI
## 26

## SAT
## 27

## SUN
## 28

# APR / MAY

**MON**
**29**

**TUE**
**30**

**WED**
**1**

**THU**
**2**

**FRI**
**3**

**SAT**
**4**

**SUN**
**5**

# MAY

**MON**
**6**

EARLY MAY BANK HOLIDAY

**TUE**
**7**

**WED**
**8**

**THU**
**9**

**FRI**
**10**

**SAT**
**11**

**SUN**
**12**

# MAY

**MON**
**13**

**TUE**
**14**

**WED**
**15**

**THU**
**16**

**FRI**
**17**

**SAT**
**18**

**SUN**
**19**

# MAY

**MON
20**

**TUE
21**

**WED
22**

**THU
23**

**FRI
24**

**SAT
25**

**SUN
26**

# MAY / JUN

**MON 27**

SPRING BANK HOLIDAY

**TUE 28**

**WED 29**

**THU 30**

**FRI 31**

**SAT 1**

**SUN 2**

# JUNE

**MON**
**3**

---

**TUE**
**4**

---

**WED**
**5**

---

**THU**
**6**

---

**FRI**
**7**

---

**SAT**
**8**

---

**SUN**
**9**

# JUNE

**MON**
**10**

**TUE**
**11**

**WED**
**12**

**THU**
**13**

**FRI**
**14**

**SAT**
**15**

**SUN**
**16**

FATHER'S DAY (UK)

# JUNE

**MON**
**17**

---

**TUE**
**18**

---

**WED**
**19**

---

**THU**
**20**

---

**FRI**
**21**

---

**SAT**
**22**

---

**SUN**
**23**

# JUNE

**MON**
**24**

**TUE**
**25**

**WED**
**26**

**THU**
**27**

**FRI**
**28**

**SAT**
**29**

**SUN**
**30**

# JULY

**MON**
**1**

**TUE**
**2**

**WED**
**3**

**THU**
**4**

**FRI**
**5**

**SAT**
**6**

ISLAMIC NEW YEAR BEGINS

**SUN**
**7**

# JULY

**MON**
**8**

---

**TUE**
**9**

---

**WED**
**10**

---

**THU**
**11**

---

**FRI**
**12**

PUBLIC HOLIDAY (NORTHERN IRELAND)

---

**SAT**
**13**

---

**SUN**
**14**

# JULY

**MON**
**15**

**TUE**
**16**

**WED**
**17**

**THU**
**18**

**FRI**
**19**

**SAT**
**20**

**SUN**
**21**

# JULY

**MON**
**22**

**TUE**
**23**

**WED**
**24**

**THU**
**25**

**FRI**
**26**

**SAT**
**27**

**SUN**
**28**

# JUL / AUG

**MON**
**29**

**TUE**
**30**

**WED**
**31**

**THU**
**1**

**FRI**
**2**

**SAT**
**3**

**SUN**
**4**

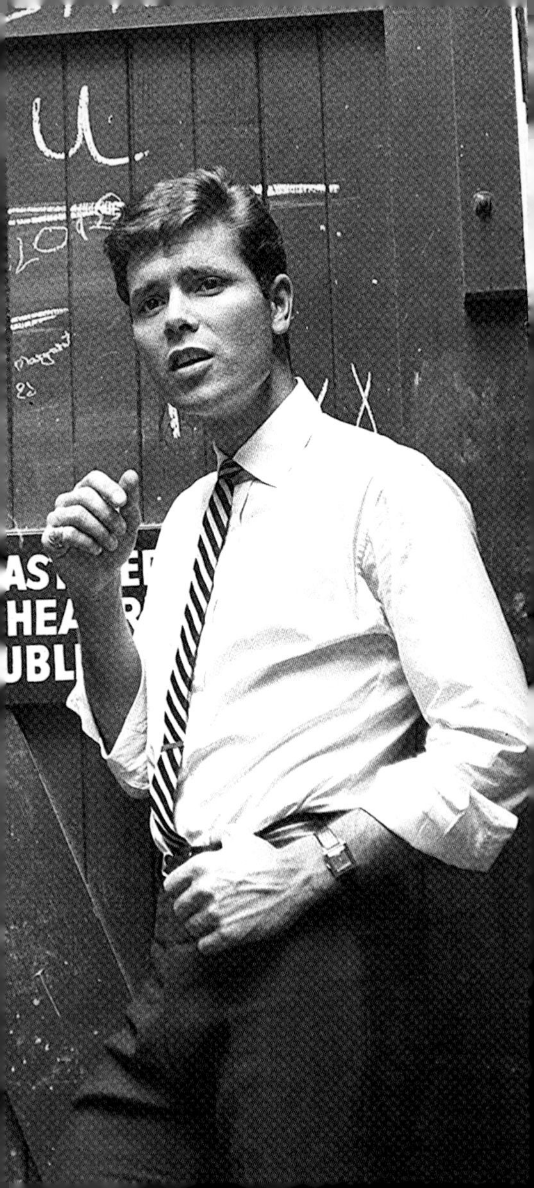

# AUGUST

**MON 5**

SUMMER BANK HOLIDAY (SCOTLAND)

**TUE 6**

**WED 7**

**THU 8**

**FRI 9**

**SAT 10**

**SUN 11**

# AUGUST

**MON**
**12**

**TUE**
**13**

**WED**
**14**

**THU**
**15**

**FRI**
**16**

**SAT**
**17**

**SUN**
**18**

# AUGUST

**MON**
**19**

**TUE**
**20**

**WED**
**21**

**THU**
**22**

**FRI**
**23**

**SAT**
**24**

**SUN**
**25**

# AUG / SEP

**MON 26**

SUMMER BANK HOLIDAY (ENG, NIR, WAL)

**TUE 27**

**WED 28**

**THU 29**

**FRI 30**

**SAT 31**

**SUN 1**

# SEPTEMBER

**MON**
**2**

**TUE**
**3**

**WED**
**4**

**THU**
**5**

**FRI**
**6**

**SAT**
**7**

**SUN**
**8**

# SEPTEMBER

**MON**
**9**

**TUE**
**10**

**WED**
**11**

**THU**
**12**

**FRI**
**13**

**SAT**
**14**

**SUN**
**15**

# SEPTEMBER

**MON**
**16**

**TUE**
**17**

**WED**
**18**

**THU**
**19**

**FRI**
**20**

**SAT**
**21**

INTERNATIONAL DAY OF PEACE (UNITED NATIONS)

**SUN**
**22**

# SEPTEMBER

**MON**
**23**

**TUE**
**24**

**WED**
**25**

**THU**
**26**

**FRI**
**27**

**SAT**
**28**

**SUN**
**29**

# SEP / OCT

**MON**
**30**

**TUE**
**1**

**WED**
**2**

ROSH HASHANAH (JEWISH NEW YEAR) BEGINS

**THU**
**3**

**FRI**
**4**

**SAT**
**5**

**SUN**
**6**

# OCTOBER

**MON**
**7**

---

**TUE**
**8**

---

**WED**
**9**

---

**THU**
**10**

WORLD MENTAL HEALTH DAY

---

**FRI**
**11**

YOM KIPPUR BEGINS

---

**SAT**
**12**

---

**SUN**
**13**

# OCTOBER

**MON 14**

LIFF'S BIRTHDAY

**TUE 15**

**WED 16**

**THU 17**

**FRI 18**

**SAT 19**

**SUN 20**

# OCTOBER

**MON**
**21**

**TUE**
**22**

**WED**
**23**

**THU**
**24**

**FRI**
**25**

**SAT**
**26**

**SUN**
**27**

DAYLIGHT SAVING TIME END

# OCT / NOV

**MON**
**28**

**TUE**
**29**

**WED**
**30**

**THU**
**31**

HALLOWEEN

**FRI**
**1**

DIWALI

**SAT**
**2**

**SUN**
**3**

# NOVEMBER

**MON**
**4**

**TUE**
**5**

GUY FAWKES NIGHT

**WED**
**6**

**THU**
**7**

**FRI**
**8**

**SAT**
**9**

**SUN**
**10**

REMEMBRANCE SUNDAY

# NOVEMBER

**MON**
**11**

**TUE**
**12**

**WED**
**13**

**THU**
**14**

**FRI**
**15**

**SAT**
**16**

**SUN**
**17**

# NOVEMBER

**MON**
**18**

**TUE**
**19**

**WED**
**20**

**THU**
**21**

**FRI**
**22**

**SAT**
**23**

**SUN**
**24**

# NOV / DEC

**MON**
**25**

**TUE**
**26**

**WED**
**27**

**THU**
**28**

**FRI**
**29**

**SAT**
**30**

ST. ANDREW'S DAY

**SUN**
**1**

# DECEMBER

**MON**
**2**

**TUE**
**3**

**WED**
**4**

**THU**
**5**

**FRI**
**6**

**SAT**
**7**

**SUN**
**8**

# DECEMBER

**MON**
**9**

**TUE**
**10**

**WED**
**11**

**THU**
**12**

**FRI**
**13**

**SAT**
**14**

**SUN**
**15**

# DECEMBER

**MON**
**16**

**TUE**
**17**

**WED**
**18**

**THU**
**19**

**FRI**
**20**

**SAT**
**21**

**SUN**
**22**

# DECEMBER

**MON
23**

**TUE
24**

**WED
25**

CHRISTMAS DAY

**THU
26**

BOXING DAY

**FRI
27**

**SAT
28**

**SUN
29**

# DEC / JAN 25

**MON**
**30**

**TUE**
**31**

NEW YEAR'S EVE

**WED**
**1**

**THU**
**2**

**FRI**
**3**

**SAT**
**4**

**SUN**
**5**

# JANUARY 25

**MON**
6

**TUE**
7

**WED**
8

**THU**
9

**FRI**
10

**SAT**
11

**SUN**
12

# CONTACTS

**NAME:**
.......................................................

**ADDRESS:**
.......................................................

.......................................................

.......................................................

**PHONE:**
.......................................................
**E-MAIL:**
.......................................................

**NAME:**
.......................................................

**ADDRESS:**
.......................................................

.......................................................

.......................................................

**PHONE:**
.......................................................
**E-MAIL:**
.......................................................

# CONTACTS

**NAME:**

.....................................................................................................................

**ADDRESS:**

.....................................................................................................................

.....................................................................................................................

.....................................................................................................................

**PHONE:**

**E-MAIL:**

.....................................................................................................................

**NAME:**

.....................................................................................................................

**ADDRESS:**

.....................................................................................................................

.....................................................................................................................

.....................................................................................................................

**PHONE:**

**E-MAIL:**

.....................................................................................................................

# CONTACTS

**NAME:**

**ADDRESS:**

**PHONE:**

**E-MAIL:**

**NAME:**

**ADDRESS:**

**PHONE:**

**E-MAIL:**

# CONTACTS

**NAME:**

**ADDRESS:**

**PHONE:**

**E-MAIL:**

**NAME:**

**ADDRESS:**

**PHONE:**

**E-MAIL:**

# CONTACTS

**NAME:**

.......................................................................................

**ADDRESS:**

.......................................................................................

.......................................................................................

.......................................................................................

.......................................................................................

**PHONE:**

.......................................................................................

**E-MAIL:**

.......................................................................................

**NAME:**

.......................................................................................

**ADDRESS:**

.......................................................................................

.......................................................................................

.......................................................................................

.......................................................................................

**PHONE:**

.......................................................................................

**E-MAIL:**

.......................................................................................

# CONTACTS

**NAME:**

...................................................................................

**ADDRESS:**

...................................................................................

...................................................................................

...................................................................................

**PHONE:**

**E-MAIL:**

...................................................................................

**NAME:**

...................................................................................

**ADDRESS:**

...................................................................................

...................................................................................

...................................................................................

**PHONE:**

**E-MAIL:**

...................................................................................

# CONTACTS

**NAME:**

**ADDRESS:**

**PHONE:**

**E-MAIL:**

**NAME:**

**ADDRESS:**

**PHONE:**

**E-MAIL:**

# NOTES

# NOTES

# NOTES

# NOTES

# NOTES

# NOTES